No More Peas, PLEASE

Illustrated by Lynn Armstrong Coffin

Learn to Tell Time.

How long does it take to eat the green peas?

Dedicated to Little Jak,
who loves his green peas!

Library of Congress Cataloging in Publication Data
Coffin, Lynn Armstrong

No More Peas, PLEASE

Printed in the USA

I do NOT like green peas,
I really do not.

time＿＿:＿＿

I will try just a few,
    but please not alot!

time __:__

If I eat the green peas,
    I'll develop a chill.
And red spots on my legs...
    really, I will!

My arms will shrink up
to half normal size!

time __:__

And my nose will curl up
between my two eyes!

time ___:___

If I eat the green peas,
if more than a few...
my foot will expand and
pop out of my shoe!

time ___:___

The hair on my head will
stick out on the side!

time___:___

And my belly will swell up
to three feet wide!

time___:___

If I eat the green peas,
   if I try one or two...
and begin turning green,
   oh! what will I do?
My hands will get shorter,
   and fatter, and bumpy.
Would you like to see me with
   knees that are lumpy?

time __:__

Can I eat them tomorrow?
    Or maybe next year?
I promise I'll love peas by then,
    Mother dear!
Today I'll eat potatoes
    and a carrot or two...
If you don't make me eat all
    my peas up for you!

time __ : __

If I eat the green peas...
if I eat them real slow...
If I try one or two...
then may I please go?

time __ : __

May I have lots of butter to
spread on my peas?
And a little more pepper and
salt if you please?

Mother...I'm eating them now.
I'm chewing them slow.
WOW! Green peas really do taste
very good, you know!

time __ : __   time __ : __

Are my arms shrinking up?
Is my hair sticking out?
If you see that I'm changing...
oh, will you please shout?

I've finished my peas, Mother.
Please may I stop?
I can't eat anymore now.
I'm ready to pop!

time __ : __

But, I do like the peas, Mother...
    really I do!
I just can't eat anymore
    now for you.

time __:__

I don't want to change.
I like me this way.
So, no more pease, please,
for just this one day!

time __:__

What time is it NOW?

time __ : __

How long did it take for him
to finish his peas?